Maths
Key Stage 2 Practice F

Steve Mills and Hilary Koll

CW00952546

Write your name and school below before you start using this book.

First Name

Last Name

School

Summary of practice paper scores

After you have finished each test and had it marked, write your test scores in these boxes.

Maths Test A

Maths Test B

Mental Maths test

Total

Note for teachers and parents

The Schofield & Sims Practice Papers have been written by teachers, for use at school and at home. Both design and content are similar to the National Curriculum Key Stage tests (SATs) used in schools. You can ensure that the practice papers are used properly by reading the introduction (page 2) and the instructions on page 5 and at the start of each test. Help the child by timing the test sessions, by reading aloud the Mental Maths test questions (see pages 45 and 46) and by marking the completed papers (full instructions and mark schemes are supplied). You can get an idea of the educational level at which the child is working using the charts on page 47. The separate Revision Guide (cross-referenced at the foot of each practice paper page) enables children to revise independently for the tests: see back cover for full details.

Schofield&Sims

Contents

As explained in the Introduction, there are three practice papers in this book. The questions for Maths Test A and Maths Test B appear on the practice papers. The third paper is a Mental Maths test, and the questions are read aloud to you by an adult. Instructions for all three tests are given on page 5 (opposite).

These are the parts of the book that you will need to use as you work through the practice papers:

The book also contains the following pages, which are best used by an adult:

This page needs to be cut out from the book by an adult, just before the Mental Maths test begins.

Schofield&Sims

Maths

Key Stage 2

Practice Papers

For school and home

■

Based on the
Primary Framework
for mathematics

Introduction

This book contains three practice papers. They will test your skills in maths. Use them to practise for the maths tests at the end of Year 6.

How to use the Maths Key Stage 2 Practice Papers

- Decide when you are going to take one of the practice papers, and ask an adult to keep that time free to help you. **Do not look at any of the papers before then.**

What you will need

Equipment:

- a pen or pencil
- a rubber
- a ruler
- a protractor
- a clock or watch for Tests A and B (all the tests are timed)
- a calculator for Test B.

Adult help:

- to make sure that you spend the right amount of time on each test (in the test instructions, the clock symbol shows when timing should begin ⏱)
- to read out loud the Mental Maths test – for this test, the adult will need **a clock or watch that measures accurately in seconds**
- to mark each test when you have finished it.

Before you start

- Read through the general instructions on page 5.

After taking the practice papers

- Ask an adult to mark your practice papers (using the answers on pages 38 to 44). When you have the total scores, you or the adult should write them in the boxes on page 3 (opposite).
- If there were some questions that you couldn't do, don't worry – the Schofield & Sims Revision Guide will help! At the bottom of every practice paper page, you will find some Revision Guide page numbers. Use these pages to revise the topics after you have done the test.

Published by Schofield and Sims Ltd,
Dogley Mill, Fenay Bridge, Huddersfield HD8 0NQ, UK

Tel 01484 607080
www.schofieldandsims.co.uk

First published in 2004
Copyright © Schofield and Sims Ltd 2004
Ninth impression 2010

Authors: Steve Mills and Hilary Koll
(contact@cmeprojects.com)

Steve Mills and Hilary Koll have asserted their moral right under the Copyright, Designs and Patents Act, 1988, to be identified as the authors of this work.

British Library Cataloguing in Publication Data
A catalogue record for this book is available from the British Library.

Edited by Carolyn Richardson Publishing Services
(cr@publiserve.co.uk)
Designed by Oxford Designers & Illustrators
Printed in the UK by Wyndeham Gait Ltd, Grimsby, North East Lincolnshire

ISBN 978 07217 0954 3

General instructions

Instructions for Tests A and B

- It is best to do the papers in the same order as they appear in the book. Maths Test A comes first.
- ⏱ **Maths Tests A and B are timed and each lasts 45 minutes.**
- **The adult who is helping you should start to time each paper from the moment you turn the page and start reading it.**
- Work carefully and quickly.
- If you cannot do a question, go on to the next one. If you have time, you can come back to it later.
- If you finish the test before the end, go back and check your work.
- Read the test instructions at the beginning of the practice paper.
- Follow carefully the instructions for each question.
- You need to put the answer where you see this symbol: ✏
- If you need to do any working out, you can use any space on a page.

Instructions for the Mental Maths test

- An adult will read out the questions to you. Each question is read out twice. You will not see the questions, so you have to listen very carefully.
- You work out the answer to each question in your head. Then you write down your answer on the answer sheet on page 37.
- Before you start the test, ask the adult who is reading out the questions to cut out the question sheet (page 45), along the dotted line.
- The adult will read out some more detailed instructions just before you start the test.

Marks

The numbers in the right-hand margin of each test page tell you how many marks each question is worth.

Remember

- **Don't cheat by reading the questions before the test, or by looking at the answers. If you do, your score won't be accurate.**
- **During the tests, think about each question carefully and try your best to answer it.**
- Any special instructions for each separate practice paper appear at the beginning of the paper. Read them carefully.
- Listen very carefully to any special instructions that the adult who is helping you may read aloud.

DO NOT TURN OVER THIS PAGE UNTIL YOU ARE READY TO START MATHS TEST A.

Maths Test A

Instructions

You are **not** allowed to use a calculator to answer any questions in this test.

Work carefully and quickly.

You have **45 minutes** to do Test A.

If you cannot do a question, go on to the next one. If you have time, you can come back to it later.

If you finish the test before the end, go back and check your work.

Follow carefully the instructions for each question.

You need to put your answer where you see this symbol:

If you need to do any working out, you can use any space on the page.

1 The hundreds digits are missing from two numbers in this number sentence.

　　Write what the digits could be.

$$\boxed{}\ \boxed{6}\ \boxed{5} \ + \ \boxed{}\ \boxed{8}\ \boxed{2} \ = \ \textbf{747}$$

Revision Guide links
If you need help after your test has been marked, read the following pages in the Revision Guide:
Question 1: pages 4–5

2   Fill in the missing numbers.

    $32 \div \boxed{} = 4$

    $49 - 27 = 35 - \boxed{}$

    $(4 \times 7) - 12 = 9 + \boxed{}$

3   Which **three** of these numbers leave **no remainder** when **divided by 3**?

Draw a ring around each of the three numbers.

    43   21   34   39   84

please turn over

Revision Guide links
If you need help after your test has been marked, read the following pages in the Revision Guide:
Question 2a: page 35; **Question 2b**: pages 32, 45; **Question 2c**: pages 35, 45;
Question 3: pages 16, 17

These shapes are in a repeating pattern.

The pattern continues like this.

Each shape is numbered.

Write the numbers that will be on the next two **triangles** in the pattern.

 and

Complete the sentence below.

Shape number 29 will be a square because…

....

....

....

1

1

Revision Guide links
If you need help after your test has been marked, read the following pages in the Revision Guide:
Question 4: pages 12–13

5   A shop sells different bottles of drinks.

This table shows the most popular drinks sold in the shop during one week.

drink	large	regular
blackcurrant	12	15
orange	14	12
lemon	11	18

How many **large bottles of orange** were sold during the week?

1 mark

Which flavour sold most during the week?

1 mark

6   Draw a circle around all the numbers that give an answer of **60** when **rounded to the nearest 10**.

   53   67   56   64   55   66

1 mark

please turn over

page 9 total

Revision Guide links
If you need help after your test has been marked, read the following pages in the Revision Guide:
Question 5: page 32; **Question 6**: pages 6–7

7   This is a spinner at a school fair.

Players spin the arrow to find what they will win. The spinner is a regular decagon.

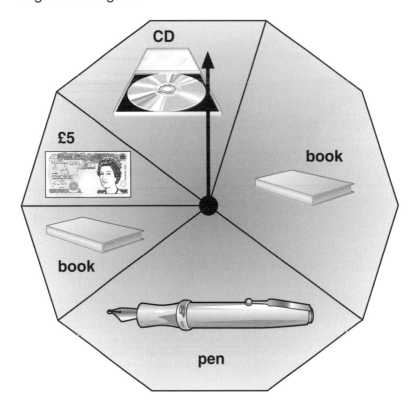

A player spins the arrow.

Which prize is the player **most likely** to win?

What is the **probability** of winning **a pen**?
Give your answer as a fraction.

Dan says, '*The probability of winning a CD is $\frac{1}{5}$*'.

Amy says, '*The probability of winning a CD is $\frac{2}{10}$*'.

Explain who you think is telling the truth and why.

    ....

Revision Guide links
If you need help after your test has been marked, read the following pages in the Revision Guide:
Question 7a: pages 77–80; **Questions 7b and 7c**: pages 19–22, 77–80

8

Mr Wood is weighing his dogs for the Dog Show.

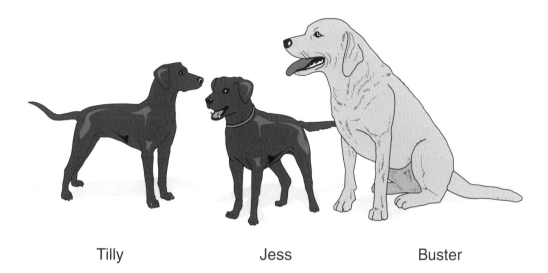

Tilly   Jess   Buster

Jess weighs $12\frac{1}{2}$ kg. Buster weighs twice as much.

How much does Buster weigh?

kg

1 mark

The three dogs together weigh exactly 50kg.

How much does Tilly weigh?

kg

1 mark

9

Calculate **815 – 462**

1 mark

please turn over

page 11
total

Revision Guide links
If you need help after your test has been marked, read the following pages in the Revision Guide:
Question 8a: pages 48, 37; **Question 8b**: page 32; **Question 9**: page 34

10 Fill in the missing number so that the numbers along each side make a total of **17**.

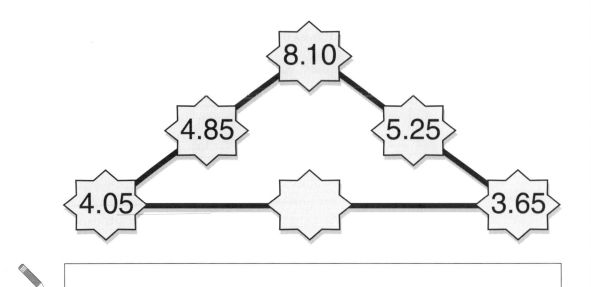

11 Deepa is describing one of the statements below.

6 more than 'three lots of P' equals twelve

Circle the statement that she is describing.

$6 + 3 + P = 17$ $9P = 12$

$6 + 3P = 12$ $6P + 3 = 12$

Revision Guide links
If you need help after your test has been marked, read the following pages in the Revision Guide:
Question 10: pages 32–34; **Question 11**: pages 46–47

12   One side of a shape has been drawn below.

The shape is a **pentagon** and it is **symmetrical**.

Draw the other sides to complete what the shape could be.

Use a ruler.

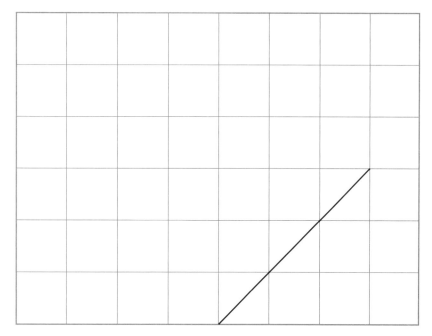

1 mark

13   Draw an arrow on this scale to show 750 grams.

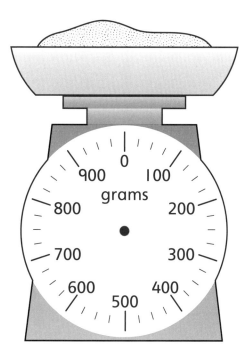

1 mark

please turn over

Schofield&Sims
Maths Key Stage 2
Practice Papers

Revision Guide links
If you need help after your test has been marked, read the following pages in the Revision Guide:
Question 12: pages 63–65, 68–69; **Question 13**: page 58

14 Here is a multiplication fact.

$$37 \times 91 = 3367$$

Use this multiplication fact to answer these questions.

 $370 \times 91 =$

 $37 \times 9.1 =$

 $37 \times 92 =$

15 Find 75% of this number.

180

Revision Guide links
If you need help after your test has been marked, read the following pages in the Revision Guide:
Question 14a: pages 6–7; **Question 14b**: pages 6–7; **Question 14c**: page 37;
Question 15: pages 26–29

16   Here is a map of the inside of a leisure centre.   **Not to scale**

| Squash court | Badminton court |
| Swimming pool | Gym |

Approximately what **fraction** of the area of the leisure centre does the **swimming pool** cover?

1 mark

The leisure centre is in the shape of a **rectangle**, where the longer side is twice the length of the shorter side.

The **shorter** side of the rectangle is **25m**.

What is the **perimeter** of the leisure centre?

   m

1 mark

please turn over

page 15 total

Schofield&Sims
Maths Key Stage 2
Practice Papers

Revision Guide links
If you need help after your test has been marked, read the following pages in the Revision Guide:
Question 16a: pages 19–20; **Question 16b**: pages 51–52

17 **Draw and shade** the reflection of this shape in the mirror line.

Use a ruler.

Mirror line

A

Each small square measures 1cm × 1cm.

What **area** of the grid is now shaded?

cm²

What **fraction** of the grid is now shaded?

How many **degrees** is angle A?

°

You may use a protractor.

Revision Guide links
If you need help after your test has been marked, read the following pages in the Revision Guide:
Question 17a: pages 68–69; **Question 17b**: pages 53–55; **Question 17c**: pages 19–20;
Question 17d: pages 73–76

18 Here is a square drawn on a coordinate grid.

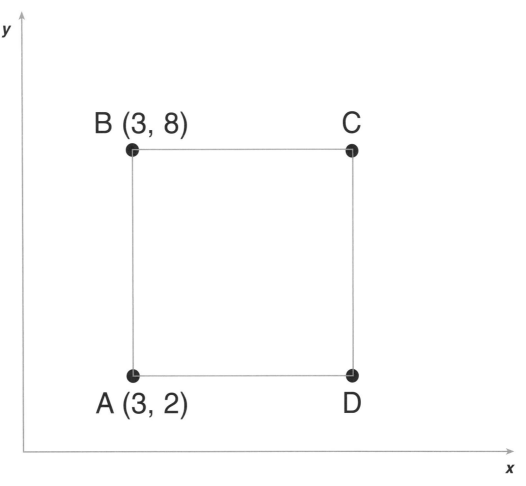

Fill in the missing **coordinates** of **points C and D.**

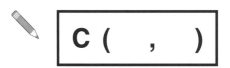

C (,)

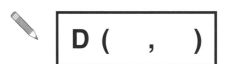

D (,)

1 mark

please turn over

page 17
total

Revision Guide links
If you need help after your test has been marked, read the following pages in the Revision Guide:
Question 18: pages 70–72

19   Look at this shape.

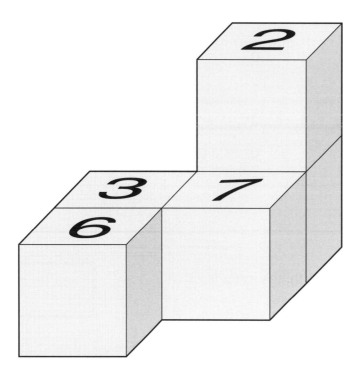

Imagine that you are looking down on the shape.

 Circle the overhead view that matches the shape.

Revision Guide links
If you need help after your test has been marked, read the following pages in the Revision Guide:
Question 19: pages 66–67

20 This table shows what six children had in their pencil cases.

Name	ruler	pencil	rubber	pen
Sanjay	0	3	1	2
Adam	1	1	2	0
James	0	0	2	3
Dan	0	1	1	1
Sam	1	2	0	2
Jane	1	3	1	0

Who had most things in their
pencil case?

This graph shows what **five** of the children had in their pencil cases.
One child's information has been left off the chart.

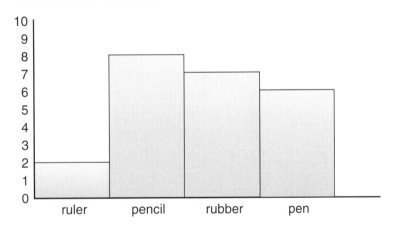

Which child's information has
been missed off the chart?

1 mark

Explain how you know this.

1 mark

please turn over

page 19
total

Revision Guide links
If you need help after your test has been marked, read the following page in the Revision Guide:
Question 20: page 81

21 Write the next two square numbers in this sequence.

 9   16   25

1 ma

22 How much milk is in the jug?

| ml |

1 r

This milk costs 44p a litre.

How much would the amount of milk in the jug cost?

| p |

1

Revision Guide links
If you need help after your test has been marked, read the following pages in the Revision Guide:
Question 21: page 18; **Question 22a**: page 57; **Question 22b**: pages 19–22

23 Jon is looking at a programme of events in an athletics meeting.

	Programme of events	
	Track	Field
7.00	Men's 5000 metres	Women's high jump
7.30	Women's 5000 metres	Men's javelin
8.00	Women's 10000 metres	↓
8.30	↓	Women's pole vault
9.00	Men's 100 metres	Men's high jump
9.30	Women's 100 metres	Women's javelin

Jon arrived at **twenty-five to eight**.

What event was on the Track
at that time?

1 mark

Jon left for a burger after **45 minutes**.

What event was on the Field
at that time?

1 mark

The women's javelin event lasted for **75 minutes**.

What time did the javelin
event end?

1 mark

page 21
total

This is the end of Maths Test A.

Total score for
Maths Test A
Write this score in
the box on page 3

Revision Guide links
If you need help after your test has been marked, read the following pages in the Revision Guide:
Question 23a: page 62; Questions 23b and 23c: pages 59–61

**DO NOT TURN OVER THIS PAGE UNTIL YOU ARE READY TO
START MATHS TEST B.**

Maths Test B

CALCULATOR ALLOWED

Instructions

You **are** allowed to use a calculator to answer questions in this test.

Work carefully and quickly.

You have **45 minutes** to do Test B.

If you cannot do a question, go on to the next one. If you have time, you can come back to it later.

If you finish the test before the end, go back and check your work.

Follow carefully the instructions for each question.

You need to put your answer where you see this symbol:

If you need to do any working out, you can use any space on the page.

1   Fill in the missing digits to make these number sentences correct.

 $\boxed{} \times \boxed{} = 376$

 $\boxed{} \div \boxed{} = 65$

Revision Guide links
If you need help after your test has been marked, read the following pages in the Revision Guide:
Question 1: pages 41–42, 45

2   Use all these digit cards once only to make this sum correct.

$$
\begin{array}{r}
\square \ \square \\
+ \quad \square \\
\square \ \square \\
\hline
6 \ 9
\end{array}
$$

please turn over

Schofield&Sims
Maths Key Stage 2
Practice Papers

Revision Guide links
If you need help after your test has been marked, read the following pages in the Revision Guide:
Question 2: pages 32 and 45

3   An arrow is pointing to each of the number lines below.

Write in the boxes the numbers that the arrows are pointing to.

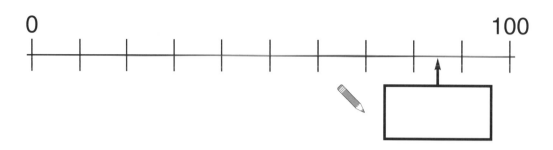

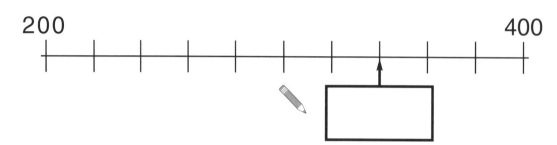

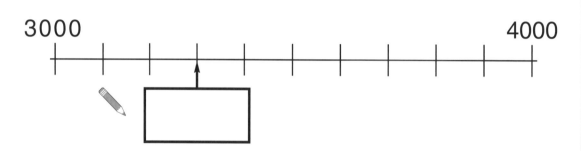

4   Lauren takes two maths tests. In Test 1 she scores 50 out of 80 and in Test 2 she scores 26 out of 40.

Write both scores as percentages.

Lauren's score for Test 1: [ ]   Lauren's score for Test 2: [ ]

3 m

1

pa
t

Revision Guide links
If you need help after your test has been marked, read the following pages in the Revision Guide:
Question 3: page 8; **Question 4**: pages 26–29

5   This cuboid is made from small cubes.

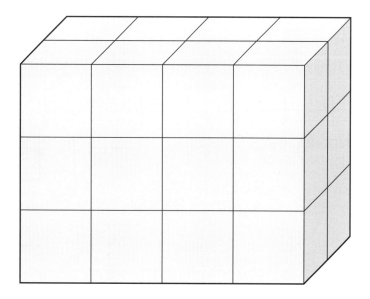

How many cubes is it made from?

1 mark

6   Put these numbers in order of size, starting with the smallest.

| 3.4 | 3.14 | 3.42 | 3.146 |

1 mark

please turn over

Schofield&Sims
Maths Key Stage 2
Practice Papers

Revision Guide links
If you need help after your test has been marked, read the following pages in the Revision Guide:
Question 5: pages 66–67, 56; **Question 6**: pages 23–24

7　Look at this number line. It shows positive and negative numbers.

The temperature was 9°C and it fell by 11°C.

What is the new temperature?

°C

1 ma

The temperature was –8°C and it rose by 12°C.

What is the new temperature?

°C

1 m

8　Measure the **longest** side of this pentagon **accurately** in **millimetres**.

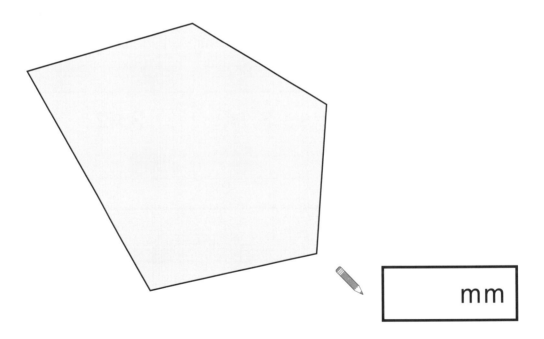

mm

1

Revision Guide links
If you need help after your test has been marked, read the following pages in the Revision Guide:
Question 7: pages 9–11; **Question 8**: pages 48–49

9

Birdseed costs £2.50 for 1kg.

Linford buys 400 grams of birdseed.

How much does he pay?

£ ⬚

1 mark

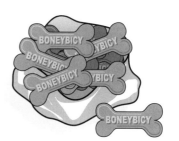

Dog biscuits cost £4.80 for 1kg.

Jennie buys a bag of dog biscuits for 60p.

How many grams of dog biscuits are in the bag?

Show your method here. You may get a mark for it. ⟹

g ⬚

2 marks

please turn over

page 27
total
⬚

Revision Guide links
If you need help after your test has been marked, read the following pages in the Revision Guide:
Question 9a: page 48–50, 19–22, 43; **Question 9b**: pages 48–50, 19–22, 41–42

10 Whitborough Castle is a tourist attraction. It gets lots of visitors.

This graph shows the number of visitors inside the castle at different times yesterday.

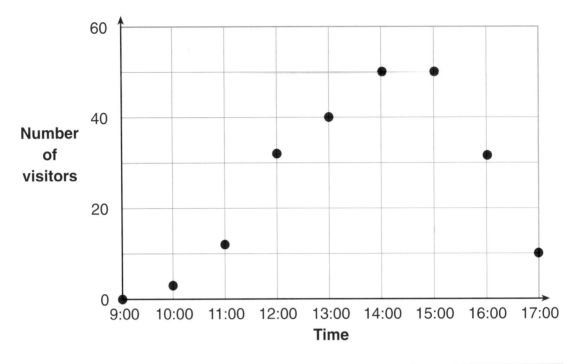

What was the approximate number of visitors at 12:00?

1 m

How many more visitors were in the castle at 12:00 than at 17:00?

1 m

Could there have been more than 50 visitors in the castle at any time? Explain your answer.

1 r

....

....

....

Revision Guide links
If you need help after your test has been marked, read the following pages in the Revision Guide:
Question 10: page 83

pa

11

Dan mixes every 3 tins of blue paint with 1 tin of white. He uses 16 tins of paint altogether.

How many of these are blue?

1 mark

Yesterday Dan mixed tins of paint in the ratio 2 white tins to every 5 blue tins. He used 8 tins of white paint.

How many tins of paint did he mix?

1 mark

12   Calculate 16% of 475

1 mark

please turn over

page 29 total

Schofield&Sims
Maths Key Stage 2
Practice Papers

Revision Guide links
If you need help after your test has been marked, read the following pages in the Revision Guide:
Question 11: pages 30–31; **Question 12**: pages 26–29

13   Write the number for each puzzle in the box.

> *I'm thinking of a number less than 20.*
>
> *It is a factor of 108.*
>
> *It is a multiple of 3.*
>
> *It is a square number.*

1 m

> *I'm thinking of a number between 10 and 30.*
>
> *It is a prime number.*
>
> *The sum of its digits is 5.*

1 r

14   A and B each stand for a whole number.

A is four times as big as B.

A plus B equals 80.

Find the values of A and B.

A =   B =

Revision Guide links
If you need help after your test has been marked, read the following pages in the Revision Guide:
Question 13a: pages 16–18; **Question 13b**: page 17; **Question 14**: pages 30–31, 46–47

15 Sanjay uses **four** number cards to make different fractions. All the fractions he makes are **less than one**.

| 6 | | 3 | | 9 | | 2 |

Show where each number card would go to make this statement correct.

Use **each** number card only **once**.

$$\frac{\boxed{}}{\boxed{}} \text{ is equivalent to } \frac{\boxed{}}{\boxed{}}$$

1 mark

16 This number sequence increases in steps of **equal size**.

Fill in the **missing numbers**.

| 7 | | | | 39 |

1 mark

please turn over

page 31 total

Revision Guide links
If you need help after your test has been marked, read the following pages in the Revision Guide:
Question 15: pages 19–22; **Question 16**: pages 12–15

17 Look at this coordinate grid.

Give the coordinates of point A.

1 ma[...]

Draw point B at **(−3, 2)**

18 Use these number cards to make a four-digit number that is a multiple of 4. Use each number card only once.

3   6   2   7

Revision Guide links
If you need help after your test has been marked, read the following pages in the Revision Guide:
Question 17: pages 70–71; **Question 18**: pages 16–17

19 Look at the shapes on the grid.

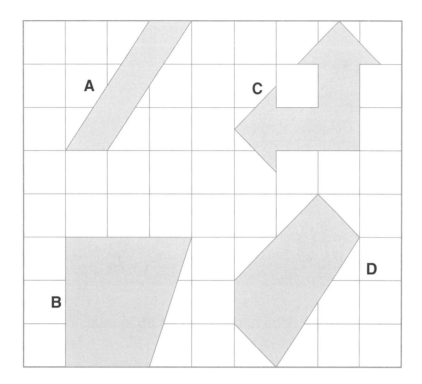

Write **one** of the letters into each sentence to make it correct.

Shape ☐ is a pentagon.

1 mark

Shape ☐ is a parallelogram.

1 mark

Shape ☐ has reflective symmetry.

1 mark

20 Ian has £*y*.
He spends £9.

Write an expression to show
how many pounds he has now.

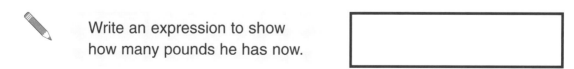

1 mark

please turn over

page 33
total

Revision Guide links
If you need help after your test has been marked, read the following pages in the Revision Guide:
Question 19: pages 63–65, 68–69; **Question 20**: pages 46–47

21   Lucy spent an afternoon at the theme park.

Rides	
Laser	£2.60
Mars	£1.25
Star	£3.00

She went on all the rides and spent **£14.55** in total. This included three rides on the Laser.

How many times did she go on the Mars ride?

1 m

22   Here are five number cards. One of them is face down.

6	4	7	9	

The mean of the five numbers is 7.

What is the number on the fifth card?

1

Revision Guide links
If you need help after your test has been marked, read the following pages in the Revision Guide:
Question 21: pages 43–45; **Question 22**: page 87

23 Write what the **missing numbers** could be to make the number sentences correct.

Make **each number** in a number sentence **different**.

 4 × ☐ × ☐ = 192

1 mark

 ☐ ÷ ☐ = 49 ÷ 7

1 mark

 −27 + 43 − ☐ = 6 × ☐

1 mark

please turn over

page 35
total

Schofield&Sims
Maths Key Stage 2
Practice Papers

Revision Guide links
If you need help after your test has been marked, read the following pages in the Revision Guide:
Question 23a: page 37; **Question 23b**: page 38; **Question 23c**: pages 10–11

24 These rectangular paving slabs surround a pond.

All the paving slabs are identical in size and shape.

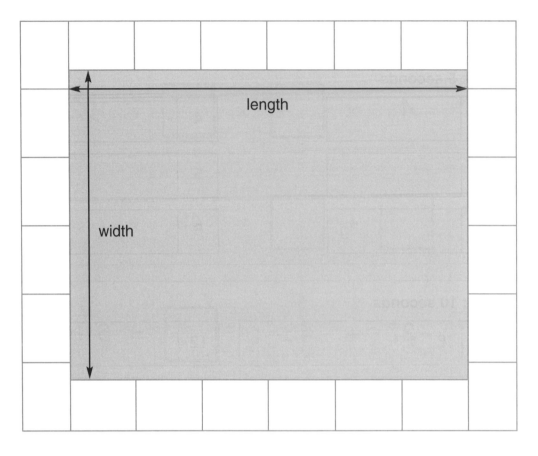

75cm

55cm [ ]   This shows the length and width of one paving slab.

Calculate the length and width of the pond in metres.

Length [m]

Width [m]

1 m

1

pa
to

This is the end of Maths Test B.

Total score for
Maths Test B
Write this score in
the box on page 3

Schofield&Sims
Maths Key Stage 2
Practice Papers

Revision Guide links
If you need help after your test has been marked, read the following pages in the Revision Guide:
Question 24: pages 43–45

Mental Maths test answer sheet

The adult who is helping you will read out the questions to you. They are on the cut-out page 45. Listen carefully.

Time: 5 seconds

1	

4	

2	

5	

3	g

6	

total for
5-second
questions

Time: 10 seconds

7	£

12	

8	

13	$17 + x = 28$	

9	cm

14	9.4kg 900g 9.15kg 8950g 9500g

10	29, 21, 13, 5, ...

15	2 3 5 8 8	

11	

total for
10-second
questions

Time: 15 seconds

16	

18	6.5 × 4.5 5.5 × 7.5 3.1 × 7.6 8.4 × 5.3

17	bus station 15:48 leisure centre 15:53 library 16:01 cinema ....

19	

20	cm

total for
15-second
questions

Mental Maths test total score
Write this score in the box on page 3

Test A answers and mark scheme

Question no.	Correct answer	Additional comments	Marks
1.	The two digits written must total 6, e.g. **565 + 182 = 747** or **465 + 282 = 747** or **365 + 382 = 747** etc.	If the child has written two digits that add to make 7, encourage him or her to add the two numbers together, e.g. 565 + 282 Point out that this gives an (incorrect) answer of **847**.	1 mark
2.	a) 8	32 ÷ 8 = 4 is the same as 8 × 4 = 32, 4 × 8 = 32 and 32 ÷ 4 = 8. Encourage the child to see the link between these facts.	1 mark
	b) 13	Children sometimes misunderstand the use of the equals sign. Rather than seeing it as an indication that what is on one side of it is of the same value as what is on the other, children sometimes see it as a sign to show the answer. Thus they become confused as 49 – 27 does not give the answer 35.	1 mark
	c) 7	The brackets indicate that the multiplication should be carried out first.	1 mark
3.	21, 39, 84	Children can be shown that the sum of the digits of all multiples of 3 have a total that is a multiple of 3, e.g. 21... 2 + 1 = 3 39... 3 + 9 = 12 84... 8 + 4 = 12	1 mark
4.	a) 10 and 14	Children should notice that the numbers on the triangles begin with 2 and are in steps of 4, i.e., 2, 6, 10, 14, 18, 22... where the difference between numbers in the sequence is 4.	1 mark
	b) An explanation that the numbers inside squares in the sequence begin with the number 1 and go up in 4s or are always one more than multiples of 4. 29 is 1 more than 28, which is a multiple of 4.	The sequence for the numbers in the squares is: 1, 5, 9, 13, 17, 21, 25, 29... where the difference between numbers in the sequence is 4. Provided that the child has given a correct explanation, with some information about the difference between terms being 4, he or she should be given a mark.	1 mark
5.	a) 14	The child should be familiar with reading information from a simple table.	1 mark
	b) lemon	The child should check the totals of each row to find which flavour sold the most.	1 mark
6.	56, 64, 55	Only these three numbers should be circled. Give no mark if fewer or more numbers are circled or if incorrect numbers are circled.	1 mark

Question no.	Correct answer	Additional comments	Marks
7.	a) book	The child is required to notice that there are two sections showing the word 'book', which together cover a greater area than the other options.	1 mark
	b) $\frac{3}{10}$	The child should notice that there are 10 equal sections on the spinner and that three of the sections have the pen prize. Thus the probability is three out of ten. Probabilities generally can be written in words or as fractions or decimals, e.g., one out of four, $\frac{1}{4}$ or 0.25	1 mark
	c) Both are telling the truth. Explanations must make reference to the fact that $\frac{1}{5}$ is the same as $\frac{2}{10}$.	These two fractions are 'equivalent' meaning that they have the same value, e.g. if you have $\frac{1}{5}$ of a pizza it is the same value (size) as $\frac{2}{10}$ of a pizza.	1 mark
8.	a) 25kg	The child should know doubles of numbers to 100 by heart and be able to deal with doubling fractions such as $\frac{1}{2}$ and $\frac{1}{4}$.	1 mark
	b) 12.5kg or $12\frac{1}{2}$ kg	The child should be using mental methods to answer this question.	1 mark
9.	353	The child should be using either mental methods or written methods to answer this question. Encourage the child to write any workings necessary in the white spaces around the question.	1 mark
10.	9.3 or 9.30	Here, the child is required to add or subtract decimals to find the missing number. The child could add 4.05 to 3.65 and then subtract the answer from 17, or could use other methods, such as counting back from 17. Remind the child that decimals can be treated in the same way as whole numbers, e.g. 4.05 + 3.65 can be answered by adding 405 and 365 and then inserting the decimal point correctly. Discuss with the child the method he or she used.	1 mark
11.	6 + 3P = 12		1 mark
12.	The shape must have 5 straight sides and at least 1 line of symmetry. Any mistakes made should be erased or crossed out.	Encourage the child to use a ruler and draw the shape accurately. Give a point for any shape that has both 5 sides and is symmetrical such as those shown below:	1 mark

Question no.	Correct answer	Additional comments	Marks
13.		Encourage the child to write other values on the scale. For more information, see the separate Revision Guide page 58.	1 mark
14.	a) 33670	Rather than calculating the answer using a written method, encourage the child to notice that this answer is 10 times larger than the given multiplication fact. A mark can be given if the correct answer was found using a different method.	1 mark
	b) 336.7	Notice that this answer is 10 times smaller than the given multiplication fact. The child could check by working out an approximate answer to decide where the decimal point should go, e.g. **37** × **9**.1 is approximately **40** × **10** = 400, so the answer is not 33.67 or 3.367, rather it is 336.7.	1 mark
	c) 3404	The child should notice that 37 × 92 is 37 more than 37 × 91. Ideally, he or she should add 37 to 3367 to get 3404. If the child finds this difficult, discuss it in a context, e.g. 37 things costing £92 each, cost £37 more than 37 things costing £91 each. A mark can be given if the correct answer was found using a different method.	1 mark
15.	135	The child should know that 75% is the same as three quarters. To find $\frac{3}{4}$ of a number mentally you could find one half, then halve the answer to find one quarter and multiply this by 3, e.g. Half of 180 = 90, Half of 90 = 45, 45 × 3 = 135. See other strategies on pages 27 and 28 of the separate Revision Guide.	1 mark
16.	a) $\frac{1}{3}$ or $\frac{2}{6}$ or an equivalent fraction.	The leisure centre plan can be divided into six equal sections, called sixths. The swimming pool area covers two such sections (two-sixths). This fraction is equivalent to one third.	1 mark
	b) 150m	Children often confuse area and perimeter. The perimeter of a shape is the distance all the way around the edge. If the shorter side of the rectangle is 25m, then the longer side is 50m, making the perimeter 25 + 50 + 25 + 50 = 150m.	1 mark
17.	a)		1 mark

Question no.	Correct answer	Additional comments	Marks
17.	b) 22cm^2	The area of a shape is the number of whole squares inside the shape. In this case it is centimetre squares or cm^2 that are counted. If children gave the answer 25, they are counting half squares as whole squares.	1 mark
	c) $\frac{22}{49}$	There should be 22 out of 49 squares shaded.	1 mark
	d) 135° Accept answers that are one degree either side of 135°, e.g. 134° or 136°.	A protractor is not essential for this question. Show the child that the angle is made from a right angle and half a right angle. Half a right angle is 90 ÷ 2 = 45°, thus the angle is 90 + 45 = 135°.	1 mark
18.	C (9, 8) D (9, 2)	Both coordinates must be correct for you to give the mark.	1 mark
19.		Some children find this type of visualisation quite difficult. If possible, make this shape with cubes and ask the child to look at the view from above (the plan) from different positions.	1 mark
20.	a) Sanjay	Sanjay had 6 items (total of numbers in first row).	1 mark
	b) Sam The child must also give an explanation of how they knew this.	The explanation should indicate some understanding that the totals of each column in the table are not the same as those in the bar chart. The child might list that 1 ruler, 2 pencils and 2 pens are missing, which is what Sam had in her/his pencil case. Any acceptable explanation with a correct answer scores 1 mark.	1 mark
21.	36, 49	This is the sequence of square numbers: 1, 4, 9, 16, 25, 36, 49. 1 × 1 = 1 2 × 2 = 4 3 × 3 = 9 4 × 4 = 16 5 × 5 = 25 6 × 6 = 36 7 × 7 = 49 … and so on.	1 mark
22.	a) 250ml		1 mark
	b) 11p	The child should know that 250ml is the same as one quarter of a litre and so find $\frac{1}{4}$ of 44p.	1 mark
23.	a) Women's 5000 metres		1 mark
	b) Men's javelin	If the child incorrectly answered Women's 10000m, point out the headings Track and Field in the table.	1 mark
	c) 10.45	75 minutes = 1 hour and 15 minutes.	1 mark

- As you mark each question on the practice paper, write the mark in the box beside it.
- Total the marks for each practice paper page, and write the page total in the box at the foot of the page.
- When you have marked every page, add up all the page totals (maximum 40 marks) and write the total in the box at the foot of page 21. Copy this total to the summary box on page 3.

Test B answers and mark scheme

Question no.	Correct answer	Additional comments	Marks
1.	a) Any 2-digit × 1-digit multiplication question with the correct answer 376, such as: 47 × 8 = 376 or 94 × 4 = 376.	The child could use the knowledge that 376 is an even number and start by dividing by 2. However, this gives a 3-digit answer. The child might then try dividing 376 by 4 to give 94. Understanding that multiplication and division are inverses is useful for such questions.	1 mark
	b) Any 3-digit ÷ 1-digit question with the answer 65, such as: 130 ÷ 2 = 65 195 ÷ 3 = 65 260 ÷ 4 = 65 325 ÷ 5 = 65 390 ÷ 6 = 65 455 ÷ 7 = 65 520 ÷ 8 = 65 585 ÷ 9 = 65	Encourage the child to see the link between multiplication and division. This means that a simple multiplication of 65 by any single digit number can provide the first number quickly. e.g. 65 × 9 = 585 so 585 ÷ 9 = 65.	1 mark
2.	Any answer where numbers total 69, i.e. where the tens digits add to make 6 and the unit digits add to make 9.	Any of the following answers are acceptable: 53 + 4 + 12 52 + 4 + 13 53 + 2 + 14 52 + 3 + 14 54 + 3 + 12 54 + 2 + 13 41 + 5 + 23 45 + 1 + 23 41 + 3 + 25 45 + 3 + 21 43 + 1 + 25 43 + 5 + 21	1 mark
3.	85, 340, 3300	Give one mark for each correct answer.	max. 3 marks
4.	Test 1: 62.5% Test 2: 65%	Give the mark only if both answers are correct. These answers can be found by: ● (Test 1) dividing 50 by 80 and multiplying by 100 ● (Test 2) dividing 26 by 40 and multiplying by 100.	1 mark
5.	24 cubes	If the child incorrectly answered 26 or 20 or 18, he or she is counting the parts of the cubes that are visible. Encourage the child to think of this as a 3-D shape and to count each layer and the number of layers altogether.	1 mark
6.	3.14, 3.146, 3.4 and 3.42	If the child gave the incorrect answer 3.4, 3.14, 3.42 and 3.146, he or she does not yet fully understand the nature of decimals. The number of digits of a decimal does not determine its size. For more information, see pages 23 and 24 of the separate Revision Guide.	1 mark
7.	a) −2°C	Counting back 9°C from 9°C will bring you to zero. Counting back 11°C from 9°C will take you to −2°C.	1 mark
	b) 4°C	Counting on 8°C from −8°C will bring you to zero. Counting on 12°C from −8°C will take you to 4°C.	1 mark
8.	68mm	Give one mark for answers between 67mm and 69mm.	1 mark

Question no.	Correct answer	Additional comments	Marks
9.	a) £1 or £1.00 Money answers must be written correctly for questions of this type. Amounts of money should never be written with both the **£** sign and a **p** sign.	Here the child is required to know that 400g is four-tenths or two-fifths of 1kg. He or she then needs to find four-tenths or two-fifths of £2.50. One fifth is £2.50 ÷ 5 = 50p, so two-fifths is 50p × 2 = £1.	1 mark
	b) 125g	Encourage the child to change the amounts of money so that they are either in pounds or in pence, rather than a mixture of the two. 60p is one eighth of 480p. So one eighth of 1kg (1000g) is 1000g ÷ 8 = 125g. Award 1 mark if there has been some attempt to divide £4.80 by 60p or to find one eighth of 1kg.	max. 2 marks
10.	a) 32	Give 1 mark for answers between 31 and 33 inclusive.	1 mark
	b) 22	Give 1 mark for answers between 21 and 23 inclusive.	1 mark
	c) Yes. For a mark to be given the explanation must include reference to the fact that between the 'hours' we don't know how many people were in the castle, e.g. between 14:00 and 15:00 there may have been more than 50 visitors.	Discuss with the child that the information shown on the graph only shows the visitor numbers 'on the hour', e.g. at 9:00, 10:00, 11:00 and so on.	1 mark
11.	a) 12	He uses 12 blue tins and 4 white tins.	1 mark
	b) 28	He mixed 20 blue tins and 8 white tins, making 28 tins altogether.	1 mark
12.	76	This could be calculated by dividing 16 by 100 and multiplying by 475.	1 mark
13.	a) 9	9 is a factor of 108, a multiple of 3 and a square number.	1 mark
	b) 23	23 is prime and 2 + 3 = 5.	1 mark
14.	A = 64, B = 16	Only give a mark if both answers are correct and the right way round, so do *not* give the mark for the answer A = 16, B = 64.	1 mark
15.	$\frac{2}{3}$ and $\frac{6}{9}$ or $\frac{3}{9}$ and $\frac{2}{6}$	The fractions can be in any order, e.g. $\frac{6}{9}$ and $\frac{2}{3}$ or $\frac{2}{6}$ and $\frac{3}{9}$.	1 mark

Question no.	Correct answer	Additional comments	Marks
16.	15, 23, 31	All numbers must be correct. The sequence goes up in steps of 8.	1 mark
17.	a) (3, 1)	The phrase 'Along the corridor and up or down the stairs' can help to remind the child that the first coordinate, e.g. −3, means across 3 to the left, and the second coordinate, e.g. 2, means 2 up.	1 mark
	b)		1 mark
18.	A four-digit number ending with the digits 32, 36, 72 or 76.	Possible answers are: 7632, 6732, 7236, 2736, 3276, 2376, 6372, 3672.	1 mark
19.	a) D	D is a pentagon.	1 mark
	b) A	A is a parallelogram.	1 mark
	c) C	C has a diagonal line of symmetry.	1 mark
20.	$y - 9$		1 mark
21.	3	3 Laser rides = £7.80 leaving £6.75, which must be 3 Mars rides and 1 Star ride.	1 mark
22.	9	For the mean to be 7, the total must be 7 × 5 cards = 35. The total of the numbers is 26, so the fifth card must be 9.	1 mark
23.	a) Any two different numbers that multiply to make 48, e.g. 24 and 2.	Note that 12 × 4 is not acceptable as all numbers must be different.	1 mark
	b) Any different numbers that divide to make 7.	Answers could include 14 ÷ 2, 21 ÷ 3, 28 ÷ 4, 35 ÷ 5, 42 ÷ 6. Note that 49 ÷ 7 is not acceptable (see above).	1 mark
	c) Any numbers that make this correct, e.g. 4 and 2, 10 and 1.		1 mark
24.	a) 4.5m	Do not give a mark for the answer 450 as this is not given in metres.	1 mark
	b) 3.4m	Do not give a mark for the answer 340 as this is not given in metres.	1 mark

- As you mark each question on the practice paper, write the mark in the box beside it.
- Total the marks for each practice paper page, and write the page total in the box at the foot of the page.
- When you have marked every page, add up all the page totals (maximum 40 marks) and write the total in the box at the foot of page 36. Copy this total to the summary box on page 3.

Mental Maths test questions and answers

Before you start

- Before you start the Mental Maths test, cut out this page along the dotted line. This will allow the child taking the test to write his or her answers on page 37 of the Practice Papers book.
- Make sure that you have **a clock or watch that measures accurately in seconds**.

During the test

- When the child is ready to start the test, make sure that he or she has the Practice Papers book open at page 37.
- Read out all the text that appears in bold below.
- Make sure that the back of this sheet is not visible to the child when you are reading from it.

After the test

- Mark the child's completed answer sheet using the answers on the back of this sheet.
- Give one mark for each correct answer.
- Add the marks to find the child's total score, and write this in the score box on page 3.
- If the child had difficulty with any of the questions, see the separate Revision Guide: pages 32, 37 and 38 cover mental arithmetic, and other sections will also be relevant.

The test

When you are ready to start the test session, read aloud the following:

I am going to read some questions to you. There are 20 questions. You have to write down the answers in the spaces on the answer sheet. Work them out in your head. You can jot things down, but don't write down all your workings out, because this will waste time. Some of the information you need is already written down for you on the answer sheet. Listen carefully when I read out the questions. I will read each one twice. If you can't answer it, put a cross in the answer box. If you make a mistake, cross it out. Then write the correct answer next to it.

Now we are ready to start the test. For this first set of questions you have *5 seconds* **to work out each answer and write it down.**

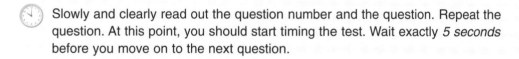 Slowly and clearly read out the question number and the question. Repeat the question. At this point, you should start timing the test. Wait exactly *5 seconds* before you move on to the next question.

1	What is the product of nine and seven?
2	Two numbers have a total of one thousand. One of the numbers is three hundred and fifty. What is the other number?
3	How many grams are there in three-quarters of a kilogram?
4	The time is quarter past seven in the evening. Write this time as it would be shown on a twenty-four hour digital clock.
5	What is nought point seven as a fraction?
6	What is ninety per cent as a decimal?

please turn over

For the next set of questions you have *10 seconds* to work out and write down each answer.

7	How much change would you get from five pounds if you spent exactly three pounds twenty-five pence?
8	One third of a number is nine. What is the number?
9	Two lengths add to make one metre. One of the lengths is thirty-seven centimetres. What is the other length?
10	Look at the number sequence on your answer sheet. What is the next number?
11	A TV programme lasts for fifty-five minutes. It starts at seven thirty. At what time does it end?
12	Two numbers have a difference of one point six. One number is four point five. What could the other number be?
13	Look at the answer sheet. In the equation, what is the value of x?
14	Look at the answer sheet. Circle the number that is nearest to nine kilograms.
15	Look at the answer sheet. What is the median of the numbers?

For the next set of questions you have *15 seconds* to work out and write down each answer.

16	A man was born in 1887. In what year was the man's ninety-fifth birthday?
17	Look at the answer sheet. It takes twenty-seven minutes to get from the leisure centre to the cinema. At what time does the bus arrive at the cinema?
18	Which of the expressions on your answer sheet has the answer nearest to thirty? Put a ring around it.
19	Which number is exactly half way between these two numbers: *five thousand two hundred* and *six thousand*?
20	Each of the sides of an octagon is one point two centimetres in length. What is its perimeter?

Tell the child: **Now put down your pen or pencil. The test is finished.**

Answers to the Mental Maths test

1	63		11	8:25 or 8.25
2	650		12	6.1 or 2.9
3	750		13	11
4	19:15 or 19.15		14	8950g
5	$\frac{7}{10}$		15	5
6	0.9 or .90		16	1982
7	£1.75		17	16:20 or 16.20
8	27		18	6.5 × 4.5
9	63cm		19	5600
10	−3		20	9.6cm

How to convert scores to levels

National Curriculum levels measure a child's progress in each subject. Each level is like one step. As children continue their education, they move up through the levels. Children within Key Stage 2 are working at a level somewhere between levels 2 and 5. Schools encourage children to reach level 4 by the end of Key Stage 2 (Year 6, age 10/11 years).

You can get an idea of the level a child is working at from the total scores that he or she obtains on the practice papers. First, you need to write the child's scores in the left-hand boxes below. You can copy these scores from the boxes on page 3.

	Score	Level	
Maths Test A			**Test A level**
Maths Test B			**Test B level**
Mental Maths			**Mental Maths test level**
Total Key Stage 2 Maths Practice Papers score			**Overall maths level**

Overall level

You can use the chart below to work out the child's overall level. The National Tests are levelled according to the child's total score. In the National Tests, the number of marks needed to gain a particular level changes each year. Nevertheless, this chart will give you some idea of the approximate level that the child is working at.

Child's total score (maximum 100)	24 or below	25–51	52–79	80+
Level	Level 1/2	Level 3	Level 4	Level 5

Looking separately at the three maths practice papers

These charts will give you an idea of the separate levels that the child may be working at in the separate papers. Use the three separate scores in the boxes that you filled in above.

Test A

Child's total score in Test A (maximum 40)	10 or below	11–20	21–31	32–40
Level	Level 1/2	Level 3	Level 4	Level 5

Test B

Child's total score in Test B (maximum 40)	10 or below	11–20	21–31	32–40
Level	Level 1/2	Level 3	Level 4	Level 5

Mental Maths test

Child's total score in Mental Maths test (maximum 20)	4 or below	5–10	11–15	16–20
Level	Level 1/2	Level 3	Level 4	Level 5

Please note

The level obtained from the Schofield & Sims Key Stage 2 Maths Practice Papers is only valid if the child is nearing the end of Key Stage 2 and has done each test under proper test conditions, without reference to the separate Revision Guide or other maths materials.

The level obtained is only an *indication* of the level at which the child is working, and it may not match the level given by the child's teacher.

The Schofield & Sims Revision Guides help children to revise for the Key Stage tests (SATs) by guiding them through what they have already learned at school on a topic-by-topic basis. The Guides have been written by teachers and are designed for children to use independently at home or in school. They are comprehensive and provide excellent value for money.

The **Key Stage 2 Maths Practice Papers** contained in this book are similar in both appearance and content to the actual Key Stage 2 mathematics tests and give children a valuable opportunity to prepare for them. The papers included are:

- Maths Test A   • Maths Test B   • Mental Maths test

Full instructions and detailed mark schemes are provided, together with tables that give an indication of the level at which the child is working. Each page is cross-referenced to the separate Key Stage 2 Maths Revision Guide, which children can refer to for help.

Also available:

The full range of Schofield & Sims Revision Guides and Practice Papers is shown here.

At Key Stage 1

Revision Guide
ISBN 978 07217 0951 2

Practice Papers
ISBN 978 07217 0952 9

Revision Guide
ISBN 978 07217 1121 8

Revision Guide
ISBN 978 07217 1120 1

At Key Stage 2

Revision Guide
ISBN 978 07217 0953 6

Practice Papers
ISBN 978 07217 0954 3

Revision Guide
ISBN 978 07217 0955 0

Practice Papers
ISBN 978 07217 0956 7

Revision Guide
ISBN 978 07217 0957 4

Practice Papers
ISBN 978 07217 0958 1

For further information, see **www.schofieldandsims.co.uk** or **telephone 01484 607080**

ISBN 978-07217-0954-3

9 780721 709543

£2.95
(Retail price)
Key Stage 2
Age range: 7–11 years

FSC
Mixed Sources
Product group from well-managed
forests and other controlled sources
Cert no. TT-COC-002542
www.fsc.org
© 1996 Forest Stewardship Council